WISHING YOU A VERY HAPPY NEW YEAR

MM.X.VIII

AMICALEMENT

love

Pierre and Silvia

OFF PISTE

OFF PISTE

OLIVER PRESTON.

For Vivien

First published in Great Britain in 2017 by

BEVERSTON PRESS

Tetbury, Glos GL8 8TT

British Library cataloguing in Publication Data
A catalogue record for this title is available from The British Library

ISBN 978-0-9549936-7-2

Designed by boinggraphics.co.uk
Printed by Gutenberg Press, Malta

"...but he's only just recovered from his broken arm."

"Gstaad. The annual test for visitors in pronouncing the name of the village."

INTRODUCTION

As we drive up the winding valleys to Gstaad, crowned by cathedrals of snow, a voice from the back of the car pipes up, "Are we nearly home yet?"

My children spent seven full winters at the John F Kennedy School in Saanen, a pretty village adjacent to Gstaad and the chirpy question reminds me that the village is very much their second home. For me, being half Swiss, the Bernese Oberland has always been a family home; skiing and skating in winter, swimming and walking in summer, but soaking up the vast mountain panorama throughout the year. I ski when it's sunny and draw when it snows. But bad news – my skiing has seen a debacle this year when, for the first time, both children skied faster than me. I cherish the many close (and international) friendships we have all made. We see our friends in the lobby at the Gstaad Palace, in private chalets or the many lucullan restaurants and clubs that scatter the village and mountain peaks.

Most visitors take the train up from Montreux, in wagons that are full of skiers, tourists, commuters and students. It is a beautiful journey that zig zags between earth and sky. The trains have themed locomotives – awarded pseudonyms by the Preston children – the chocolate train, the papercut train, the Golden Pass and the train with the Bernese bears. They run all hours and are never late. On arrival, their passengers are disgorged into the pretty hauptstrasse of Gstaad, with its plethora of shops - *Hermès, Ralph Lauren, Cartier, Chopard* and *Lorenz Bach* and some new chalet arrivals - *Louis Vuitton, Dolce & Gabbana*, and *Graff*. They may be challenging on the wallet, but make excellent viewing for the late afternoon 'passeggiata', after taking tea and cakes in the excellent cafés.

I produce some of my best work when drawing in Gstaad. When I was eighteen I had a chance meeting with the celebrated author Sir Laurens Van der Post, who was in the habit of staying at the Posthostel Rössli. Every year he would go there to start a new book. He said that, 'he found the sea and mountains very productive for writing.' I also met Professor John Galbraith who was a regular winter visitor. Galbraith was author of "The Affluent Society", and goodness, Gstaad must have provided some rich material. I drew this book in Gstaad, and rich residents and their relationships with the locals have always provided inspiration for my cartoons. From nonagarian heiresses ruminating over their wills, (with problems you'd like to have), to Simmental farmers with one sick cow – the drawings are merely a gentle satire of the village. Maybe some of the Gstaadois will recognize themselves in a few of the cartoons.

More so than ever I pursue the adage that you need three things in life – something to work on, someone to love, or love you, and something to look forward to. As I sit in my studio in England, taking in the Cotswolds in spring, the buds blossoming and lambs frollicking in the fields, I cannot help but look forward to my next visit to Gstaad, to its flowers in May, its glorious summer and its first flakes of winter snow.

OLIVER PRESTON.

"Now you see why we wanted a chalet near the Palace Hotel."

"The Morning After"

OLIVER PRESTON.

"Can you please wait until the last skier has left the course?"

"...and if she misbehaves take away her
cigarettes and alcohol for a week."

"My parents sent me to the school because it's named after a bottle of wine."

"It's quiet. Too quiet."

"Can you tell my husband he's here to pick up our children. Not girls."

*"Have you seen the queue for the lift?
We may have to ski down."*

"Not rabbit. Last time he had rabbit, he ate it."

"Ladies, LADIES, please. It's only a handbag."

"Next time bend your knees."

"Now, try and relax."

"It's so big my husband had it engraved with the price."

"If the train is late ONE MORE TIME there will be consequences."

"I'm sure we had him with us when we went down to the village."

"Darling, there's something I need to tell you."

"I'm so sorry, we thought you had a bigger jet."

"But mummy, some helpless poor creature has to suffer so I can have this..."

"Don't worry darling, your father won't get the bill for a couple of weeks..."

"Now I understand why she needs two fur coats."

"...and it's ski in ski out..."

OLIVER PRESTON.

"It's not quite the sort of star spotting I had in mind."

"...not the champagne and truffle fondue!"

"I'm afraid this lunch is about to go downhill."

"I thought you said your friends could ski."

"My husband's from Geneva. He sells watches."

"Everyone thinks you're really hot."

"Hello, I didn't recognise you without your ski suit on."

"Papa, you should have worn a helmet."

" It does 0-60 in under three seconds."

"After lunch we're doing the Wasserngrat, Wispile and the Videmanette."

"You don't love me anymore. You no longer laugh at my joke."

"Dammit woman, I'm not made of plastic."

"I can't wait to tell my husband that I've skied off-piste."

"That was great. Shall we do it again?"

LE GRAND BELLEVUE

*"For one horrible moment I thought
you would have to hire a second jet."*

"She looks amazing for 100 years old."

*"After three long weeks,
Hans was nearly finished."*

OLIVER PRESTON.

"We won't be coming out today. We're telly skiing."

"Darling, is that you having a pee behind the ski lift?"

"Are we nearly there yet?"

"Yo mummy! You're trending on Twitter, Facebook and Instagram...'

"So monsieur, were we practising the slalom for tomorrow's race?"

"Gstaad Palace,
New Year 2013"

*"Gstaad Palace,
New Year 2016"*

"Gstaad puts its first cow on the moon."

OLIVER PRESTON.

"There's a much better party over on the Oberbort."

"You'll never guess WHO we've just seen from the chairlift."

"I know I'm going to heaven, because I've already
been to hell trying to teach you to ski."

"If you could learn how to cook
we could get rid rid of the chef."

"If you were better in bed we
could get rid of my ski instructor."

72

"Unter Gstaad or Ober Gstaad ?"

"Well, at least we can afford the heating this year."

"Look after the millions and the hundreds of millions
will look after themselves."

OLIVER PRESTON.

"The Greeks have gone skiing in Gstaad."

"I'm frightfully sorry. I don't speak Swiss German."

"It's cheaper storing her here than letting
her loose on the shops in Gstaad."

"I'll have what
he's having."

"What are you two looking so smug about?"

"You've missed the last lift. I'm afraid you're stuck for the night."

OLIVER PRESTON.

"I thought you said you had a chalet IN Gstaad?"

"What was that about putting the batty old fool in a nursing home and getting the chalet in Gstaad?"

*"They came from the moon bringing peace and goodwill.
Unfortunately they were made of cheese."*

"I know it's a marketing gimmick, but hopefully
it'll attract some local interest."

ACKNOWLEDGEMENTS

Illustration Acknowledgements
First published
12, 23, 25, 28, 37, 38, 48, 49, 51, *The Field Magazine*; 27, 34, 67, *Gstaad Palace Magazine*; 6, 11, 19, 42, 55, 57, *Gstaad My Love Magazine*.

By the same author

Liquid Limericks (2001)	*Robson Books*	*with Alistair Sampson*
Larder Limericks (2004)	*Robson Books*	*with Alistair Sampson*
Shall we join the Men (2005)	*Beverston Press*	
Modern Cautionary Verses (2006)	*Constable Robinson*	*with Charlie Ottley*
Hitting the Slopes (2008)	*Beverston Press*	
How to be Asked Again (2009)	*Quiller*	*with Rosie Nickerson*
Out of Town (2010)	*Beverston Press*	
Out for a Duck (2010)	*Quiller*	*with Ian Valentine*
Another Log on the Fire (2011)	*Beverston Press*	
Real Men Drink Port (2011)	*Quiller*	*with Ben Howkins*
Fondue and Furs (2011)	*Beverston Press*	
Rich Pickings (2013)	*Beverston Press*	
The Imperfect Shot (2015)	*Quiller*	*with Jeremy Hobson*
Lively Limericks (2015)	*Beverston Press*	*with Patrick Holden*
Raise Your Game (2016)	*Quiller*	*with Ian Valentine*
The Long Weekend (2017)	*Beverston Press*	

My thanks to Simon Russell at Boing for the design and layout preparation, To Jill Schumm at Beverston Press, Hans Ueli Tschanz and Andrea Scherz at The Gstaad Palace. To Elsbeth Preston, Vivien, Amber and Rex, and Baloo, for being such a wonderful source of ideas.

Prints and greeting cards are available from *'Off Piste'*
Visit www.beverstonpress.com or call +44 (0) 1666 502638